QUEEN

Folio ©1995 International Music Publications Ltd.,
Southend Road • Woodford Green • Essex IG8 8HN • England
Designed by Richard Gray
Music transcribed by Barnes Music Engraving Ltd. • East Sussex TN22 4HA
Printed by Panda Press • Haverhill • Suffolk
Binding by ABS • Cambridge

QUEEN

IT'S A BEAUTIFUL DAY

(Queen)

It's a beautiful day

The sun is shining

I feel good

And no-one's gonna stop me now, oh yeah

It's a beautiful day

I feel good, I feel right

And no-one, no-one's gonna stop me now

Mama

Sometimes I feel so sad, so sad, so bad

But no-one's gonna stop me now, no-one

It's hopeless – so hopeless to even try

IT'S A BEAUTIFUL DAY

Words and Music by
Queen

It's a beau-ti-ful day,_____ the sun is shin-ing, I feel

good and no-one's gon-na stop me now,_____ oh yeah.

It's a beau-ti-ful day,_____ I feel good, I feel right and

MADE IN HEAVEN

(Freddie Mercury)

I'm taking my ride with destiny

Willing to play my part

Living with painful memories

Loving with all my heart

Made in heaven, made in heaven

It was all meant to be, yeah

Made in heaven, made in heaven

That's what they say

Can't you see

That's what everybody says to me

Can't you see

Oh I know, I know, I know that it's true

Yes it's really meant to be

Deep in my heart

I'm having to learn to pay the price

They're turning me upside down

Waiting for possibilities

Don't see too many around

Made in heaven, made in heaven

It's for all to see

Made in heaven, made in heaven

That's what everybody says

everybody says to me

It was really meant to be

Oh can't you see

Yeah, everybody, everybody says

Yes it was meant to be

Yeah, yeah

When stormy weather comes around

It was made in heaven

When sunny skies break through behind the clouds

I wish it could last forever, yeah

Wish it could last forever, forever

I'm playing my role in history

Looking to find my goal

Taking in all this misery

But giving it all my soul

Made in heaven, made in heaven

It was all meant to be

Made in heaven, made in heaven

That's what everybody says

Wait and see, it was really meant to be

So plain to see

Yeah, everybody, everybody, everybody tells me so

Yes it was plain to see, yes it was meant to be

Written in the stars…

Written in the stars…

MADE IN HEAVEN

Words and Music by
Freddie Mercury

F#m
B
B7/D#
D#dim7
yeah, wish it could last for - ev - er, for - ev - er.
F
C
Am
D
G
F
D7
C
G
D
Asus4
A
F#7/A#
I'm
B
D#m
G#m
4fr
B7
play-ing my role in his - to-ry, look-ing to find my goal, tak-ing in all this mi-se-ry, but

stars,

writ-ten in the stars,

writ-ten in the stars.

LET ME LIVE

(Queen)

Why don't you take another little piece of my heart

Why don't you take it and break it

And tear it all apart

All I do is give

All you do is take

Baby why don't you give me

A brand new start

So let me live (so let me live)

Let me live (leave me alone)

Let me live, oh baby

And make a brand new start

Why don't you take another little piece of my soul

Why don't you shape it and shake it

'til you're really in control

All you do is take

And all I do is give

All that I'm askin'

Is a chance to live

(So let me live) - so let me live

(Leave me alone) - let me live, let me live

Why don't you let me make a brand new start

And it's a long hard struggle

But you can always depend on me

And if you're ever in trouble - hey

You know where I will be

Why don't you take another little piece of my life

Why don't you twist it, and turn it

And cut it like a knife

All you do is live

All I do is die

Why can't we just be friends

Stop livin' a lie

So let me live (so let me live)

Let me live (leave me alone)

Please let me live

(Why don't you live a little)

Oh yeah baby

(Why don't you give a little love...?)

Let me live

Please let me live

Oh yeah baby, let me live

And make a brand new start

Let me live (let me live)

Oh yeah (let me live)

Come on, come on (let me live)

In your heart, oh baby

(Take another piece, take another piece)

Please let me live

(Take another piece, take another piece)

Why don't you take another piece

Take another little piece of my heart

Oh yeah baby

Make a brand new start

All you do is take

Let me live

LET ME LIVE

Words and Music by
Queen

Let me live,__

please let me live,___ oh yeah ba-by   let me live__ and make a brand new__ start.

repeat to fade

(*Vocal ad lib.*)

MOTHER LOVE

(Brian May, Freddie Mercury)

I don't want to sleep with you

I don't need the passion too

I don't want a stormy affair

To make me feel my life is heading somewhere

All I want is the comfort and care

Just to know that my woman gives me sweet -

Mother Love

I've walked too long in this lonely lane

I've had enough of this same old game

I'm a man of the world and they say that I'm strong

But my heart is heavy, and my hope is gone

Out in the city, in the cold world outside

I don't want pity, just a safe place to hide

Mama please, let me back inside

I don't want to make no waves

But you can give me all the love that I crave

I can't take it if you see me cry

I long for peace before I die

All I want is to know that you're there

You're gonna give me all your sweet -

Mother Love

My body's aching, but I can't sleep

My dreams are all the company I keep

Got such a feeling as the sun goes down

I'm coming home to my sweet -

Mother Love

MOTHER LOVE

Words and Music by
Freddie Mercury and Brian May

I don't want to sleep with you,
I don't want to make no waves,

I don't need the pas-sion too
but you can give me all the love that I crave,

I don't want a storm-y af-fair,
I can't take it if you see me cry,

to make me feel my life is head-ing some-where,
I long for peace be-fore I die,

22

My bo-dy's ach-ing but I can't sleep, my dreams are all the com-pan - y I keep,

got such a feel-ing as the sun goes_ down, I'm com-ing home to my sweet_____

repeat to fade

mo-ther love._____

MY LIFE HAS BEEN SAVED

(Queen)

This is where we are today

People going separate ways

This is the way things are now

In disarray

I read it in the papers

There's death on every page

Oh Lord, I thank the Lord above

My life has been saved

Here we go, telling lies

Here we go

We're right back where we started from

People going separate ways

This is the way things are now

In disarray

I read it in the papers

There's death on every page

Oh Lord, I thank you from above

My life has been saved

My life, my life has been saved

My life, my life, my life has been saved

MY LIFE HAS BEEN SAVED

Words and Music by
Queen

My life, my life has been saved,

my life, my life, my life has been saved.

I WAS BORN TO LOVE YOU

(Freddie Mercury)

I was born to love you

With every single beat of my heart

Yes, I was born to take care of you

Every single day…

chorus:

I was born to love you

With every single beat of my heart

Yes, I was born to take care of you

Every single day of my life

You are the one for me

I am the man for you

You were made for me

You're my ecstasy

If I was given every opportunity

I'd kill for your love

So take a chance with me

Let me romance with you

I'm caught in a dream

And my dream's come true

It's so hard to believe

This is happening to me

An amazing feeling

Comin' through -

chorus

I wanna love you

I love every little thing about you

I wanna love you, love you, love you

Born - to love you

Born - to love you

Yes I was born to love you

Born - to love you

Born - to love you

Every single day - of my life

An amazing feeling

Comin' through

chorus

Yes I was born to love you

Every single day of my life

Go, I love you babe

Yes, I was born to love you

I wanna love you, love you, love you

I wanna love you

I get so lonely, lonely, lonely, lonely

Yeah, I want to love you

Yeah, give it to me

I WAS BORN TO LOVE YOU

Words and Music by
Freddie Mercury

HEAVEN FOR EVERYONE

(Roger Taylor)

This could be heaven

This could be heaven

This could be heaven for everyone

In these days of cool reflection

You come to me and everything seems alright

In these days of cold affections

You sit by me – and everything's fine

This could be heaven for everyone

This world could be fed, this world could be fun

This could be heaven for everyone

This world could be free, this world could be one

In this world of cool deception

Just your smile can smooth my ride

These troubled days of cruel rejection, hmm

You come to me, soothe my troubled mind

Yeah, this could be heaven for everyone

This world could be fed, this world could be fun

This should be love for everyone, yeah

This world should be free, this world could be one

We should bring love to our daughters and sons

Love, love, love, this could be heaven for everyone

You know that

This could be heaven for everyone

This could be heaven for everyone

Listen – what people do to other souls

They take their lives – destroy their goals

Their basic pride and dignity

Is stripped and torn and shown no pity

When this should be heaven for everyone

HEAVEN FOR EVERYONE

Words and Music by
Roger Taylor

This could be hea-ven, this could be hea-ven,

this could be hea-ven, this could be hea-ven, this could be hea-ven for ev-ery-one. In these days

of cool _____ re - flec - tion,
of cool _____ de - cep - tion,

40

TOO MUCH LOVE WILL KILL YOU

(Brian May, Frank Musker, Elizabeth Lamers)

I'm just the pieces of the man I used to be

Too many bitter tears are raining down on me

I'm far away from home

And I've been facing this alone

For much too long

I feel like no-one ever told the truth to me

About growing up and what a struggle it would be

In my tangled state of mind

I've been looking back to find

Where I went wrong

Too much love will kill you

If you can't make up your mind

Torn between the lover

And the love you leave behind

You're headed for disaster

'cos you never read the signs

Too much love will kill you

Every time

I'm just the shadow of the man I used to be

And it seems like there's no way out of this for me

I used to bring you sunshine

Now all I ever do is bring you down

How would it be if you were standing in my shoes

Can't you see that it's impossible to choose

No there's no making sense of it

Every way I go I'm bound to lose

Too much love will kill you

Just as sure as none at all

It'll drain the power that's in you

Make you plead and scream and crawl

And the pain will make you crazy

You're the victim of your crime

Too much love will kill you

Every time

Too much love will kill you

It'll make your life a lie

Yes, too much love will kill you

And you won't understand why

You'd give your life, you'd sell your soul

But here it comes again

Too much love will kill you

In the end…

In the end.

TOO MUCH LOVE WILL KILL YOU

Words and Music by
Brian May, Frank Musker
and Elizabeth Lamers

YOU DON'T FOOL ME
(Queen)

You don't fool me

You don't fool me…

Da, da da da dah

Da da da dah

Da da dah…

You don't fool me – those pretty eyes

That sexy smile – you don't fool me

You don't rule me – you're no surprise

You're telling lies – you don't fool me

Mmm, mama said be careful of that girl

Mama said you know that she's no good

Mama said be cool, don't you be no fool

Yup bup ba ba ba ba da da da dah !

You don't fool me

You don't fool me, you don't fool me

She'll take you

You don't fool me, and break you

You don't rule me, you don't fool me

You don't fool me, she'll take you

You don't fool me, and break you

Sooner or later you'll be playing by her rules

Baby you don't fool me, yeah

You don't fool me, you don't have to say 'don't mind'

You don't have to teach me things I know

Sooner or later you'll playing by her rules

Oh, (fool you) oh, (rule you) she'll take you (take you)

And break you (break you)

Yeah

Mama said be cool

Mama said she'll take you for a fool

She'll take you, and break you

Ba ba ba ba bap bap ba baah

La la la la la lah

You don't fool me

You don't fool me…

YOU DON'T FOOL ME

Words and Music by
Queen

52

Ba - by you don't

A WINTER'S TALE
(Queen)

It's Winter-fall

Red skies are gleaming - oh -

Sea-gulls are flyin' over

Swans are floatin' by

Smoking chimney-tops

Am I dreaming…

Am I dreaming…?

The nights draw in

There's a silky moon up in the sky - yeah -

Children are fantasising

Grown-ups are standin' by

What a super feeling

Am I dreaming…

Am I dreaming…?

woh-woh-woh-woh

(dreaming)

So quiet and peaceful

Tranquil and blissful

There's a kind of magic in the air

What a truly magnificent view

A breathtaking scene

With the dreams of the world

In the palm of your hand

(dreaming)

A cosy fireside chat

A little this, a little that

Sound of merry laughter skippin' by

Gentle rain beatin' on my face

What an extraordinary place!

And the dream of the child

Is the hope of the man

It's all so beautiful

Like a landscape painting in the sky - yeah -

Mountains are zoomin' higher - mm -

Little girls scream an' cry

My world is spinnin' and spinnin' and spinnin'

It's unbelievable

Sends me reeling

Am I dreaming…

Am I dreaming…?

Oooh - it's bliss.

A WINTER'S TALE

Words and Music by
Queen